How to use this book

Follow the advice, in italics, given for you on each page.

Support the children as they read the text that is shaded in cream.

Praise *the children at every step!*

Detailed guidance is provided in the Read Write Inc. Phonics Handbook

8 reading activities

Children:

- *Practise reading the speed sounds.*
- *Read the green and red words for the story.*
- *Listen as you read the introduction.*
- *Discuss the vocabulary check with you.*
- *Read the story.*
- *Re-read the story and discuss the 'questions to talk about'.*
- *Re-read the story with fluency and expression.*
- *Practise reading the speed words.*

D0326094

Speed sounds

Consonants   *Say the pure sounds (do not add 'uh').*

f (ff)	l ll	m mm	n nn kn	r rr	s ss	v ve	z zz s	(sh)	(th)	ng (nk)

b bb	c k ck	d dd	g gg	h	j	p pp	qu	t tt	w (wh)	x	y	ch (tch)

Vowels   *Say the sounds in and out of order.*

at	hen head	in	on	up	day	see happy	high	blow

zoo	look	car	for	fair	whirl	shout	boy

*Each box contains one sound but sometimes more than one grapheme. Focus graphemes are **circled**.*

4

Green words

Read in Fred Talk (pure sounds).

<u>wh</u>en   ca<u>tch</u>   dr<u>i</u><u>nk</u>   mu<u>nch</u>

<u>gr</u><u>ee</u>n   <u>kn</u><u>ee</u>   cr<u>ee</u>p   f<u>ee</u>t   str<u>ee</u>t   <u>three</u>

Read in syllables.

a`sl<u>ee</u>p → asl<u>ee</u>p        grem`lin → gremlin   gr<u>ee</u>d`y → gr<u>ee</u>dy

so<u>gg</u>`y → so<u>gg</u>y        yu<u>mm</u>`y → yu<u>mm</u>`y        se<u>tt</u>`<u>ee</u> → se<u>tt</u> <u>ee</u>

di<u>sh</u>`clo<u>th</u> → di<u>sh</u>clo<u>th</u>    co<u>ff</u>`<u>ee</u> → co<u>ff</u> <u>ee</u>

Read the root word first and then with the ending.

<u>cr</u>a<u>ck</u> → <u>cr</u>a<u>ck</u>ed   sit → si<u>tt</u>in<u>g</u>   k<u>ee</u>p → k<u>ee</u>ps

Red words

<u>the</u>   to   my   wa<u>sh</u>in<u>g</u>*

*Red word for this book only

Vocabulary check

Discuss the meaning (as used in the story) after the children have read each word.

definition:

gremlin   *funny little creature*

slops   *leftover food*

creep   *walk watchfully*

dishcloth   *a cleaning cloth*

Punctuation to note in this story:

Sam Green Grimlin	*Capital letters for names*
When	*Capital letters that start sentences*
.	*Full stop at the end of each sentence*
!	*Exclamation mark used to show excitement*
...	*Wait and see*

The greedy green gremlin

Introduction

Is your mum/dad fussy about keeping the kitchen sink clean?

I don't think Sam's mum and dad keep their sink clean.
In amongst the dishes and dirty dishcloth lives a gremlin who
loves the mess. It loves all the bits of food that people leave
at the end of a meal.

Story written by Gill Munton
Illustrated by Tim Archbold

I'm the greedy green gremlin Sam keeps in the sink

Soggy crusts to munch, yummy slops to drink!

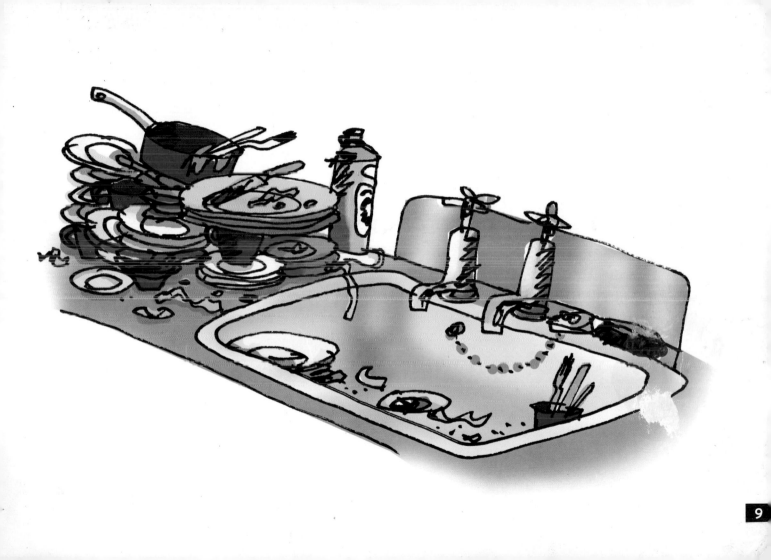

When Sam is sitting on the settee

And the cat is asleep on his knee

I creep from the tap on my three green feet,

a greedy green gremlin from Green Gremlin Street!

I sleep in the dishcloth, play catch with the plug

I keep my teeth in a cracked coffee mug

When Sam's washing dishes, it's best not to stay

I just pick up a crust, and creep away ...

Questions to talk about

Re-read the page. Read the question to the children. Tell them whether it is a **FIND IT** question or **PROVE IT** question.

FIND IT

✔ Turn to the page

✔ Read the question

✔ Find the answer

PROVE IT

✔ Turn to the page

✔ Read the question

✔ Find your evidence

✔ Explain why

Page 8:   FIND IT   *What do we know about the gremlin?*

Page 10:   FIND IT   *When does the gremlin creep from the tap?*

Page 12:   FIND IT   *Where does he sleep?*

Page 12:   FIND IT   *What does he keep in the cracked coffee mug?*

Page 12:   PROVE IT   *Why do you think he disappears when Sam is washing up?*